To my father
whose affection
for cats is
legendary

First published in hardback in Great Britain as *The Truth About Cats* by HarperCollins Publishers Ltd in 1995
First published in paperback by Picture Lions in 1996
This edition published by HarperCollins Children's Books in 2009

1 3 5 7 9 10 8 6 4 2

ISBN-13: 978-0-00-730992-4

Picture Lions is an imprint of the Children's Division, part of HarperCollins Publishers Ltd.
HarperCollins Children's Books is a division of HarperCollins Publishers Ltd.

Text and illustrations copyright © Alan Snow 1995

A CIP catalogue record for this title is available from the British Library.
Visit our website at: www.harpercollins.co.uk

Printed in China

How Cats Really Work!

by ALAN SNOW

HarperCollins *Children's Books*

Do you know where cats come from? Or what really lies beneath their soft and furry exterior? What do cats want from humans and why are dogs their enemies? To discover the fascinating story of how cats came to live on Planet Earth, what the inner workings of these curious creatures look like and why they have a secret mission, read on…

Contents

Where Do cats come From?

capital city of the Planet Nip →

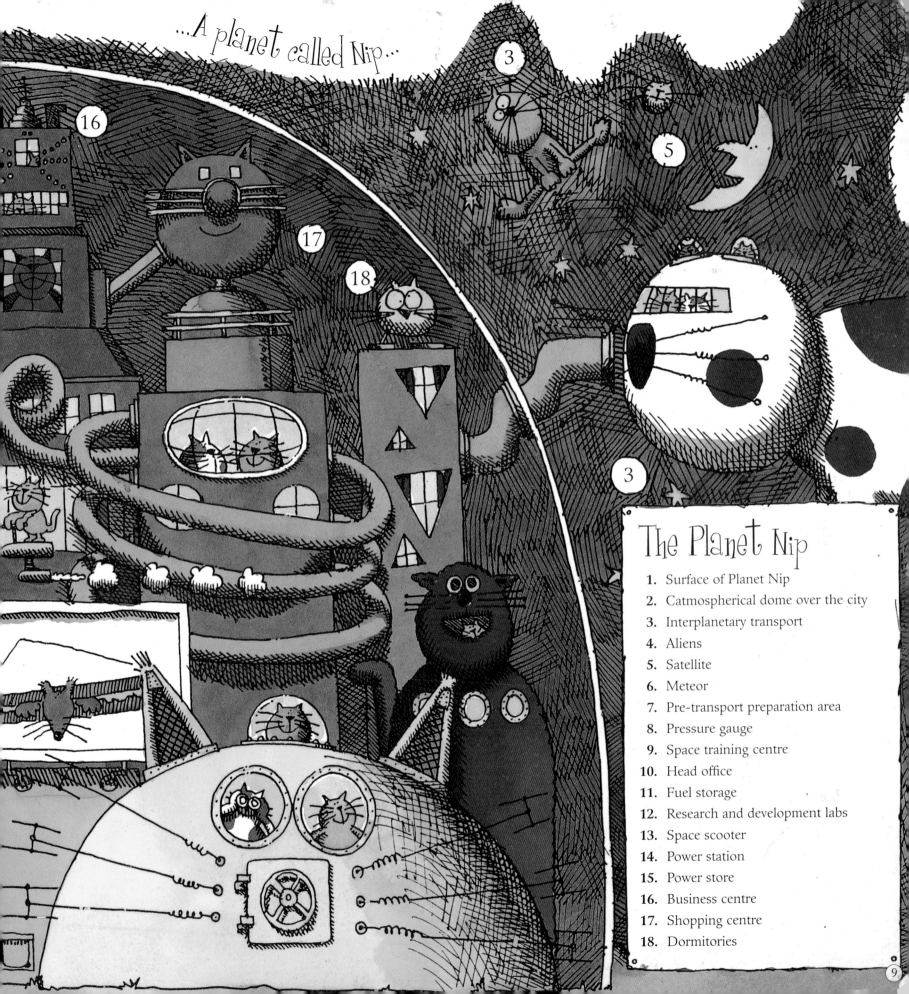

The Planet Nip

1. Surface of Planet Nip
2. Catmospherical dome over the city
3. Interplanetary transport
4. Aliens
5. Satellite
6. Meteor
7. Pre-transport preparation area
8. Pressure gauge
9. Space training centre
10. Head office
11. Fuel storage
12. Research and development labs
13. Space scooter
14. Power station
15. Power store
16. Business centre
17. Shopping centre
18. Dormitories

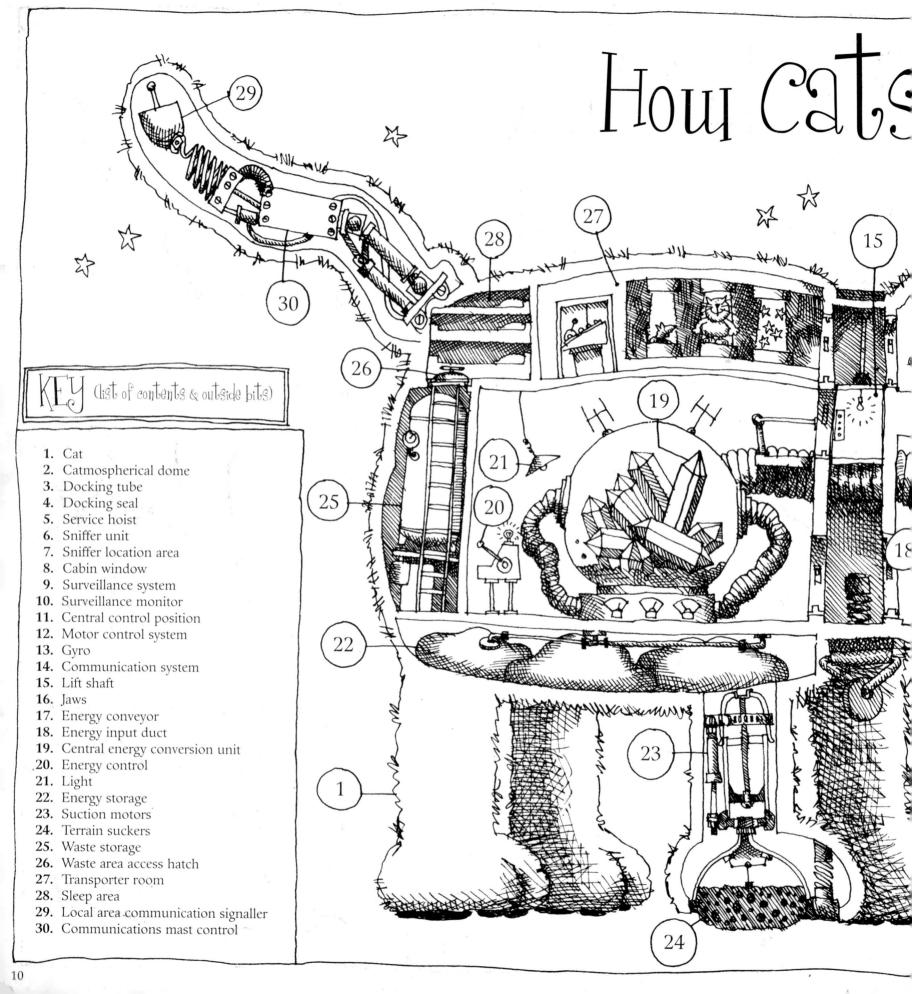

KEY (list of contents & outside bits)

1. Cat
2. Catmospherical dome
3. Docking tube
4. Docking seal
5. Service hoist
6. Sniffer unit
7. Sniffer location area
8. Cabin window
9. Surveillance system
10. Surveillance monitor
11. Central control position
12. Motor control system
13. Gyro
14. Communication system
15. Lift shaft
16. Jaws
17. Energy conveyor
18. Energy input duct
19. Central energy conversion unit
20. Energy control
21. Light
22. Energy storage
23. Suction motors
24. Terrain suckers
25. Waste storage
26. Waste area access hatch
27. Transporter room
28. Sleep area
29. Local area communication signaller
30. Communications mast control

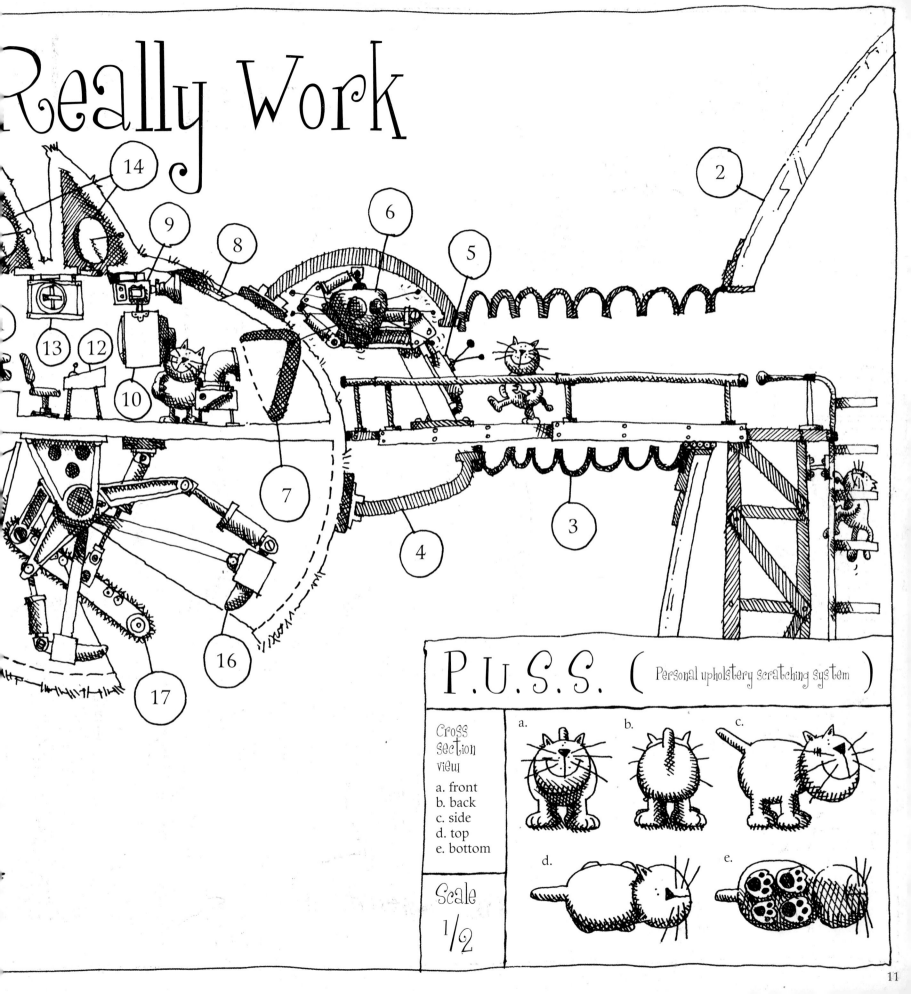

P.U.S.S. (Personal upholstery scratching system)

Cross section view

a. front
b. back
c. side
d. top
e. bottom

Scale 1/2

Mission Earth...!?!

A long, long time ago there were two races on the Planet Nip: the Canines and the Felines. The Felines made life very miserable for the Canines by jumping on their heads and forcing them to eat fish and lick themselves clean. The Canines got so tired of this that they built a primitive spaceship and set off to find a new home. After three weeks, they discovered Earth where they made friends with Humans and became known as Dogs. They settled down to a happy and comfortable life until…

communication tuner

dog scanner

lift
motor

communication headset

radar

memory
system

← lift

washing machine

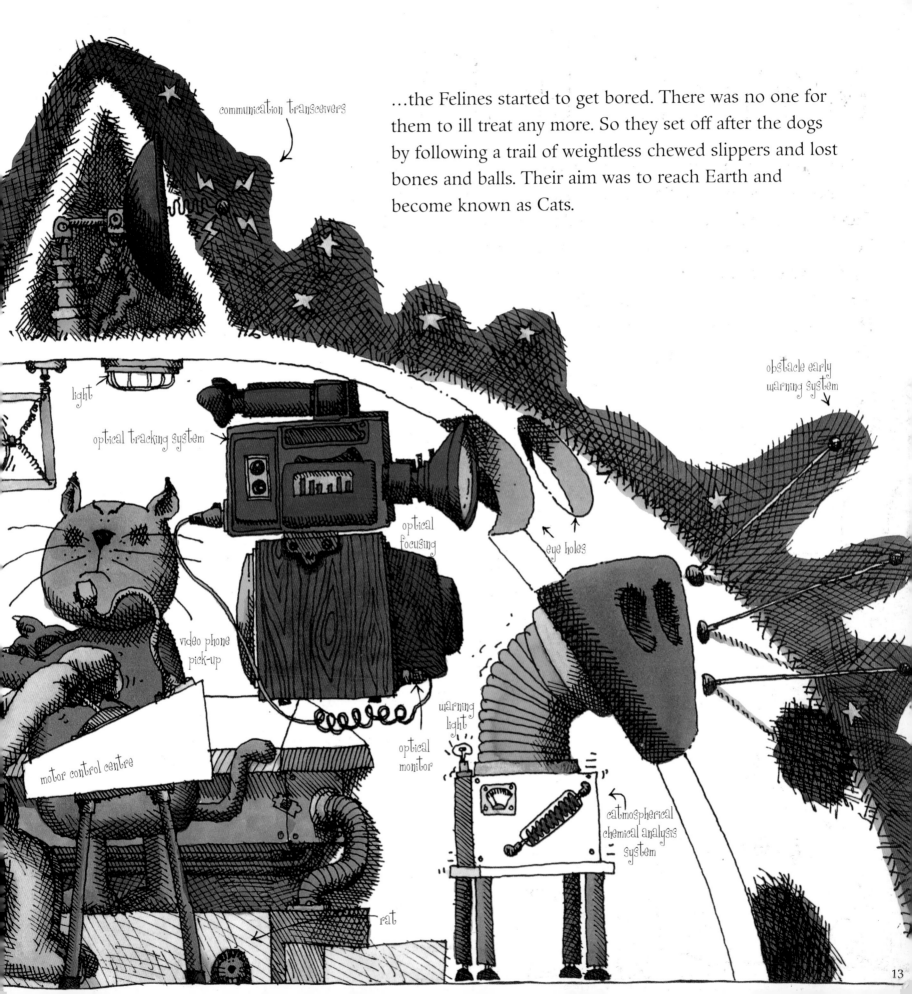

...the Felines started to get bored. There was no one for them to ill treat any more. So they set off after the dogs by following a trail of weightless chewed slippers and lost bones and balls. Their aim was to reach Earth and become known as Cats.

communication transceivers

obstacle early warning system

light

optical tracking system

optical focusing

eye holes

video phone pick-up

motor control centre

warning light

optical monitor

catmospherical chemical analysis system

rat

Space, the Final Frontier

And so the Cats made their way through the fantastic vacuum that is space, across the mighty void, weaving between stars, asteroids, planets and satellites, leaving behind the safety of home. The Cats moved ever closer to the planet Earth where the unsuspecting occupants were going about their business. Only the dogs on Earth had any idea what might happen.

Cats usually arrive at night to avoid suspicion. Cats already on Earth send out horrendously noisy signals to guide the orbiting Cats. The aim is to land on soft targets; compost heaps, rubbish dumps – and dogs! Large quantities of dirt become embedded in the Cat's outer shell taking years to remove. At any spare moment during a Cat's time on Earth, it can be seen trying to extract this debris from its upholstery with its 'paws' or 'mouth'.

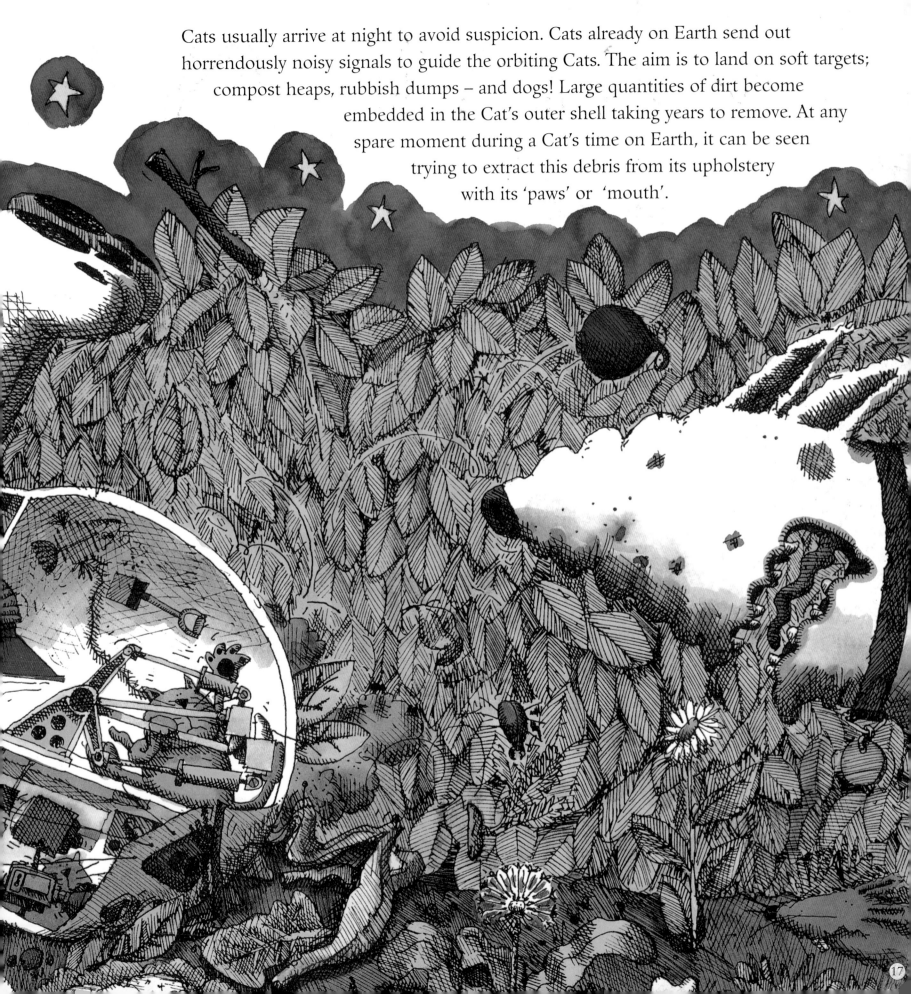

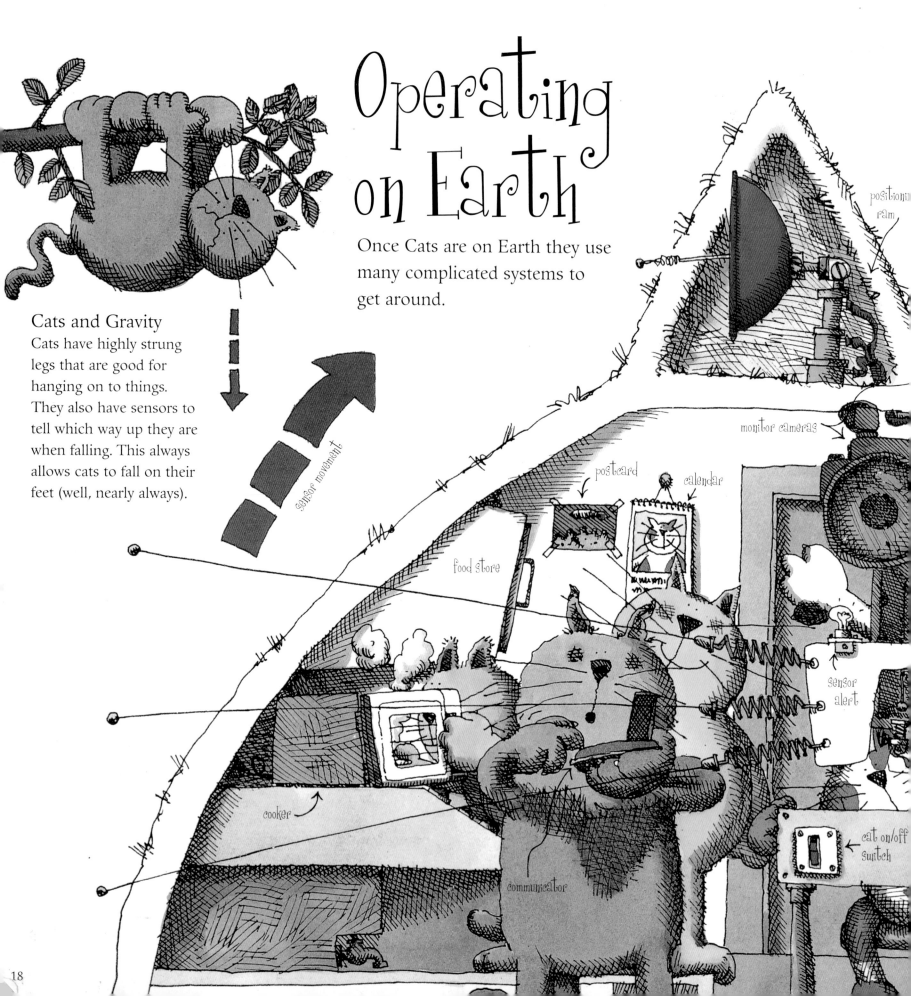

Operating on Earth

Once Cats are on Earth they use many complicated systems to get around.

Cats and Gravity

Cats have highly strung legs that are good for hanging on to things. They also have sensors to tell which way up they are when falling. This always allows cats to fall on their feet (well, nearly always).

sensor movement

positioning ram

monitor cameras

postcard

calendar

food store

sensor alert

cooker

communicator

cat on/off switch

Gyro system

Gyros are simple machines (usually a spinning fly wheel) used to check which way up things are and how tilted or wobbly they are.

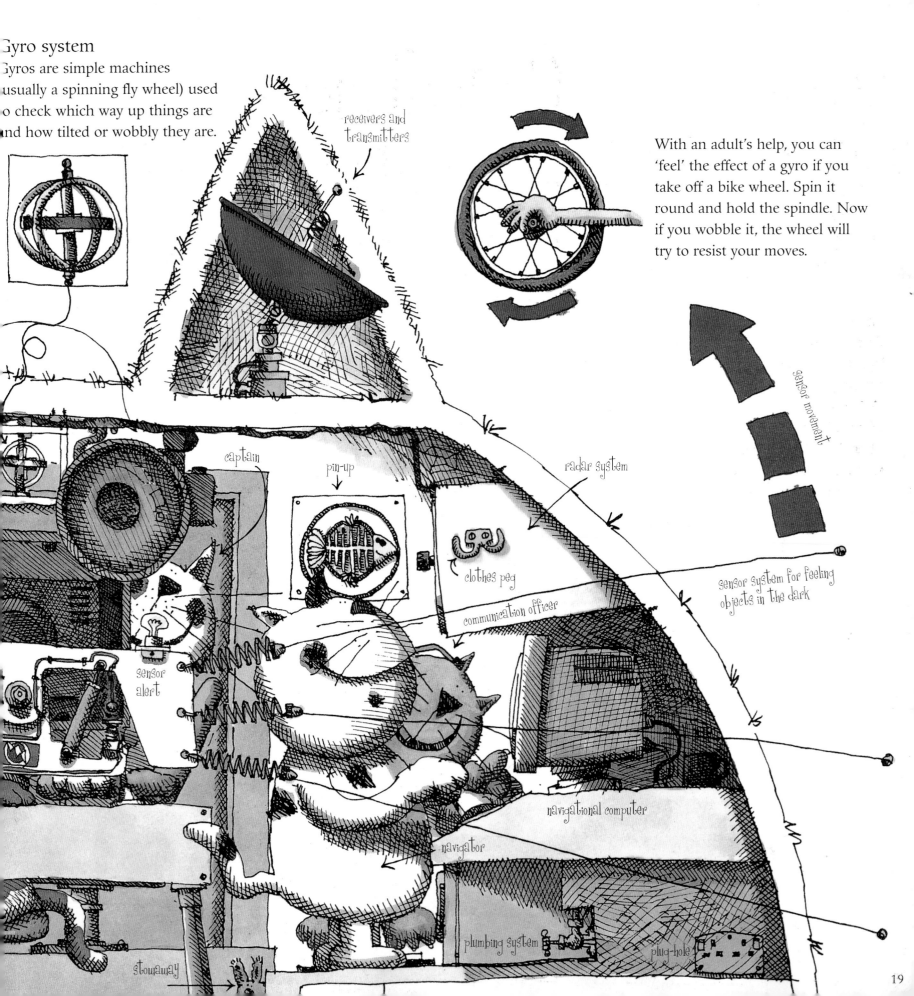

receivers and transmitters

With an adult's help, you can 'feel' the effect of a gyro if you take off a bike wheel. Spin it round and hold the spindle. Now if you wobble it, the wheel will try to resist your moves.

sensor movement

captain

pin-up

radar system

clothes peg

communication officer

sensor system for feeling objects in the dark

sensor alert

navigational computer

navigator

plumbing system

plug-hole

stowaway

Encounter...

As humans do not understand the danger, they often restrain the dogs until it is too late...

Dogs may try to communicate...

...but it is nearly always useless.

cats and Dogs

help signals
(sent out to get help!)

warning signal!!
surface
controlled to
gain volume to
give illusion of
greater size.

The secret and terrible mission of the Cats is world domination and control of all fish supplies. Their first task is to drive out all dogs. This cannot be done just by confrontation, as dogs are usually bigger than Cats. So Cats must use tactics…

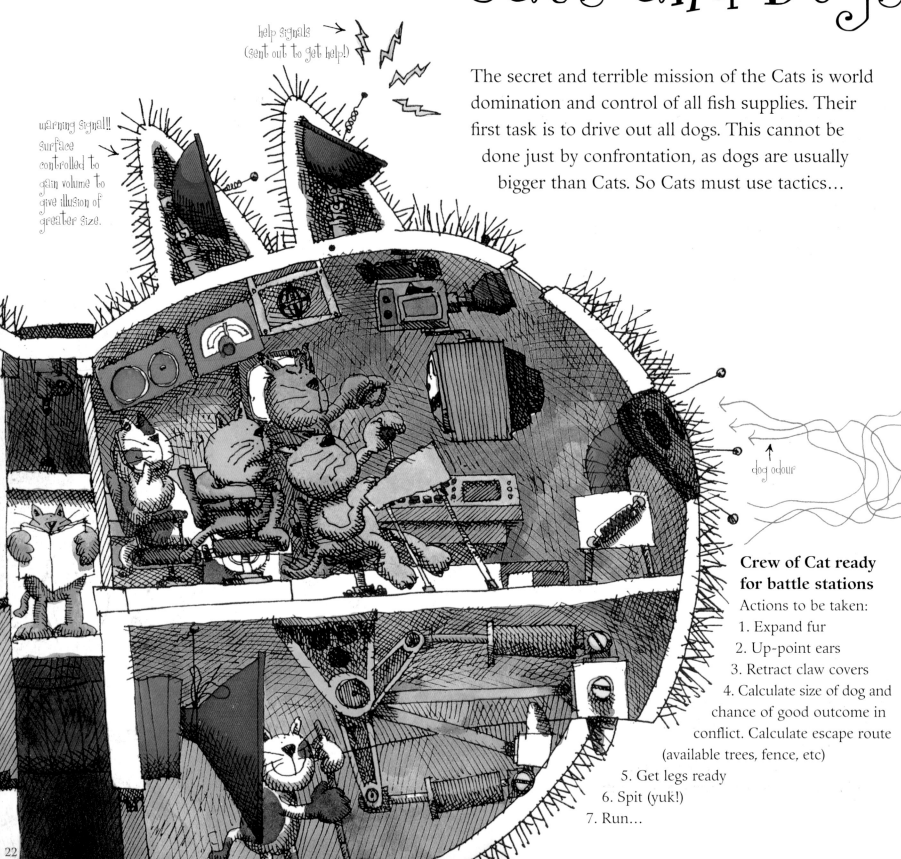

dog odour

Crew of Cat ready for battle stations
Actions to be taken:
1. Expand fur
2. Up-point ears
3. Retract claw covers
4. Calculate size of dog and chance of good outcome in conflict. Calculate escape route (available trees, fence, etc)
5. Get legs ready
6. Spit (yuk!)
7. Run…

(Part 1)

Tactic 1

Climb into tree using suction motors. Attract dog's attention.
Wait until dog has exhausted itself barking. Drop on dog's
head. Run away…

Tactic 2

Drive dog mad.
Move in with humans and gain their protection.
Jump on dog or steal its food while humans are not looking.
When dog reacts, wind your Cat body around human legs.

Tactic 3

At night, go to house where dog lives
(when dog is locked in.) Walk around
yard or garden making high pitched howling
noises that only dogs can hear.
Wait until dog has knocked him or herself
insensible on the window, trying to get you!!!

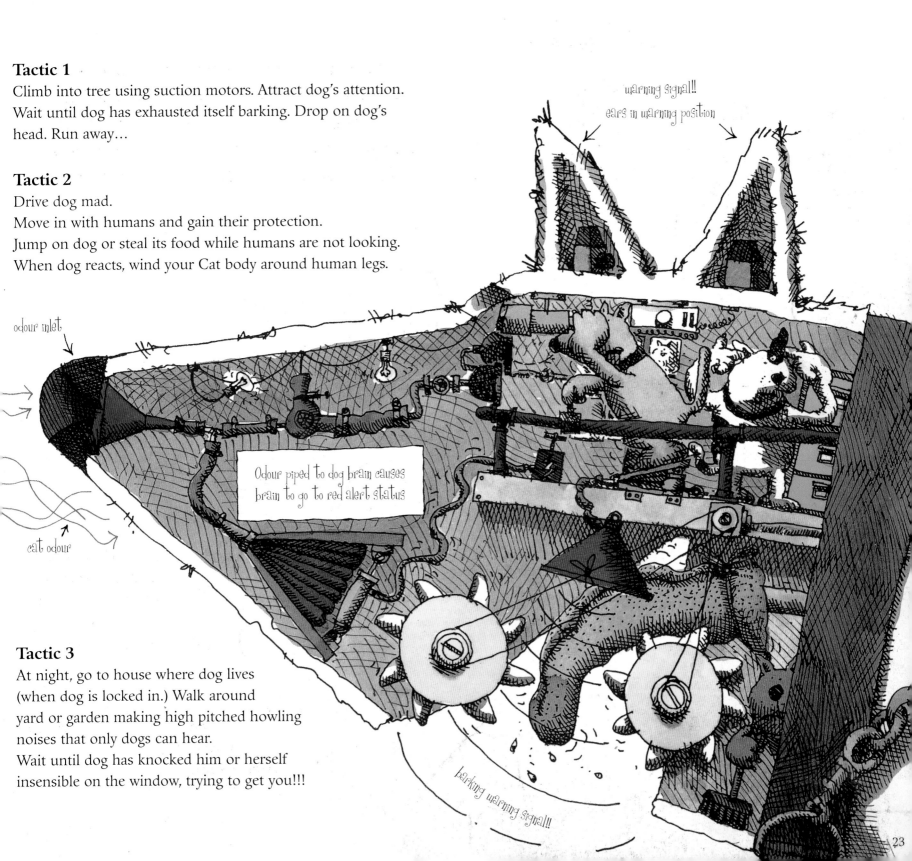

warning signal!!
ears in warning position

odour inlet

cat odour

Odour piped to dog brain causes
brain to go to red alert status

barking warning signal!!

cats and Dogs (Part 2)

I don't like it, Captain… he's too quiet… watch out for any sudden moves…

Second in Command: Duties include standing in for captain and general running of the cat.

Communication Officer: Monitors audio and radio signals and reports to Captain as well as operating weapon systems: teeth, spit and claws.

Open emergency channel… calling all Cats.

Pilot: Duties include monitoring visual path, operating legs, mouth and eating lunch.

Inside the Cat control centre the dog is monitored on the visual monitor. The monitor system can be switched to very low light levels so the Cat can operate even in darkness. The team headed by the Captain works out the best course of action…

monitor screen

dog

Don't worry… wait till he starts barking again, then full power, jump on his head and bounce over the gate!! He'll never suspect that!!

Captain:
Duties include ordering equipment, reporting back to Planet Nip and choosing lunch.

Captain, I've put up the deflector shields, but I think we only have power for another three minutes.

motor control centre

Control of Humans

Humans are very easy for Cats to control. Once power is gained over them, humans are very useful for collecting food and providing protection. They can be trained to accept comings and goings at all times of day or night. This leaves Cats free to pursue their master plan of world domination and control of all fish supplies.

Some humans add escape hatches to their own buildings, just for Cats. These should be just big enough for Cats to squeeze through but just small enough for a dog's head to get stuck. Cats may seem too big for the hole but this is just an illusion because they come from another planet space dimension!

Feeble minded person being exposed to sympathy rays...

Watch out for the following signs in humans – any of these show that a Cat is in control:

1. A weird desire to buy pretty cat collars
2. Speaking in "baby talk" to adult Cats
3. Allowing Cats to ruin expensive furniture
4. Trekking around every shop in town to find just the right brand of Cat food

Enthusiastic glow (radiation from sympathy ray)

A large number of cats supported by a single human

Some humans are feeble minded so total control can be gained easily. A large number of Cats can even be supported by a single person, their every whim catered for… fresh fish, furniture to scratch, even protection from dogs. Since the earliest of times, Cats have taken advantage of this, wheedling their way into positions of power within many homes.

Even with human help, Cats have not yet succeeded in their mission. But, day by day, they gain more power, strengthening their hold over humans and dogs. Cats roam freely while dogs are banned from many public places. Be warned – complete Cat control is not far away!

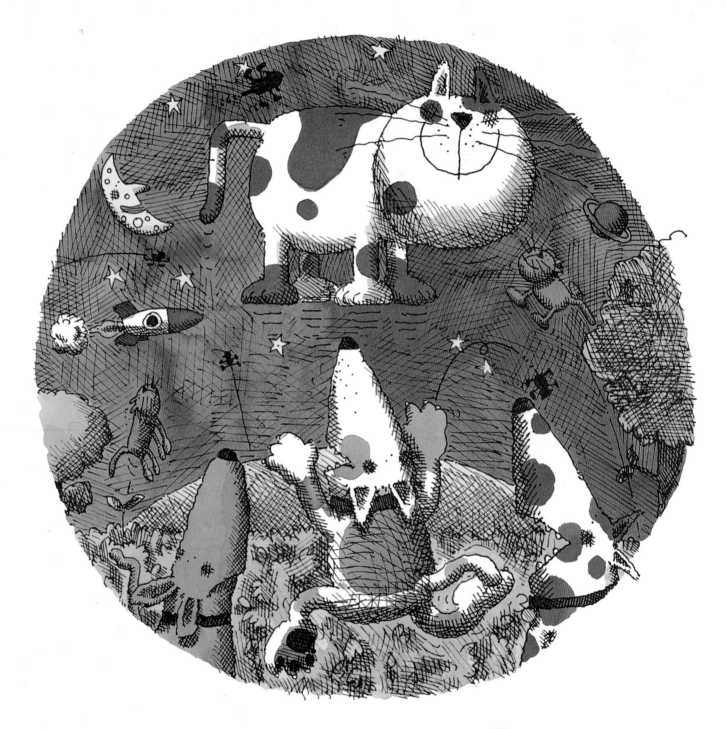

The ENd

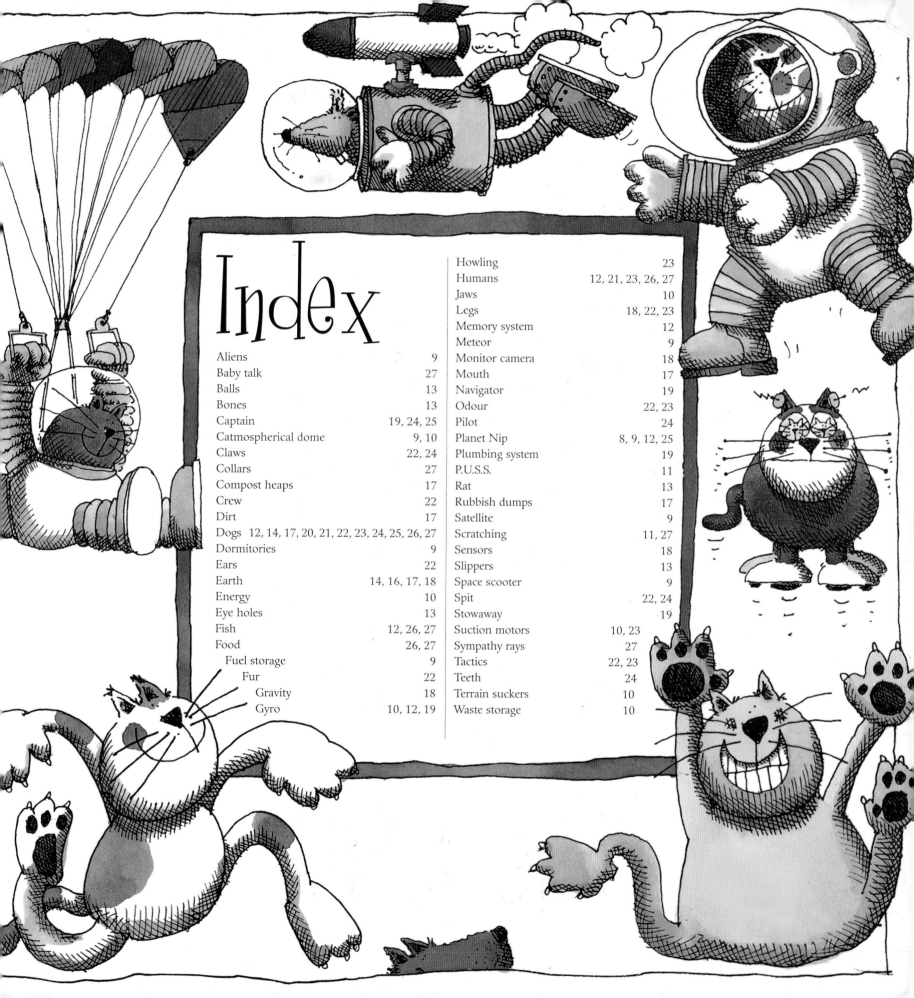

Index

Also look out for...

HoW DoGs ReallY WorK!

small memory   cat identifiers

dinner detecting sensor

barking operation unit

by
ALAN
SNOW

power supply to leg

bone-burying device

ISBN: 978-0-00-730991-7

A comical, in-depth guide to how dogs really work.
Once you've started getting your teeth into the
astonishing true facts, you'll soon be begging for
more! Essential reading for all wary pet owners.

"One of the funniest books about dogs ...
hilarious." *Books for Keeps*